BLESSINGS

STORIES, SONGS, POEMS AND PRAYERS
ON BLESSINGS IN SWANSEA

WITH A FOREWORD
BY
IRIS GOWER

WITH PHOTOGRAPHS
BY
BIDDY WIGLEY

EDITED BY RUTH JENKINS
FOR MACMILLAN CANCER SUPPORT

REGISTERED CHARITY NUMBER 261017

The cover image is
by
Biddy Wigley

Parks

Oh vivid Vivian's vivacious parks
blossom, bloom, beckon across the home town
housing many birds: wrens, robins and larks.

The leaves are like all leaves, yet exotic
brought back home from all the wide foreign world
planted and granted Welsh wet elixir.

The rain polishes and veils the Abbey.
Sunbeams play, dance, skip, glisten, shine, up and down
the grey walls of the Vivians' castle

where, in its arched porch entrance, lies SALVE
grey limestone letters boldly embossed, made
from the bones and shells of dead sea creatures

SALVE welcomes all staff and visitors
yesterday, today, tomorrow, always,
there in the Abbey, in Singleton Park

where vivid Vivian's vivacious plants
blossom, bloom, beckon as elsewhere in town
housing many birds: wrens, robins and larks.

Ruth Jenkins

This anthology is illustrated with blooms, blossoms and flowers
to remind us of the beauty and blessings of many of Swansea's parks
that were established by the Vivians.

Contents

Foreword by Iris Gower
The Story of the Misses Angels and Their Farm

Contributors:

ISBN 0-9548671-2-2

Published by Cartersford Publications Wales
First impression 2006

The sale proceeds from this book will go to:
Macmillan Cancer Support
Registered Charity No: 261017

Printed in Wales by Geoff's Print Shop, Tycoch, Swansea

ACKNOWLEDGEMENTS

The story of the Misses Angels and their Farm
(from an account by E.E. Rowse, written in 1896)
was copied from:
http://www.themumblesbook.com/history/the missesangels.htm

Thank you, Iris Gower, for writing
the foreword for Blessings, the third and final book in the
anthology of three, for Macmillan Cancer Support.

Many thanks also to Judie Thomas of JT & Co whose help
for this project is invaluable and very much appreciated

A big thank you
to Biddy Wigley
who kindly supplied the beautiful photographs
for this edition

The contributors of texts and photographs gave their work free of
charge. The cost of printing was met by arranging a kaleidoscope
of events..
Thank you for all the support received!

Ruth Jenkins
Swansea, November 2006

s Gower
ssings …

privilege and a pleasure to write the foreword for Blessings, :hird anthology in the trilogy edited by Ruth Jenkins for .millan Cancer Support.

is a Swansea woman born and bred it makes me proud to read 'n the pages of Courage and Ambition the literary work of the talented women - women who have given of their time so generously to contribute to the new publication that will bring tears and smiles to the faces of all who read it.

Some time ago I was invited to speak at the opening of the Amy Dillwyn House at the University College of Swansea. Amy was a courageous woman of her day who took on the tremendous debts, her inheritance from her father, but paid them all off and blossomed as a business woman in her own right. At the opening it was my pleasure to meet the unsung, unseen women who work on the mind blowing technical side of providing books for the blind and partially sighted.

And there was creativity in abundance in the House seen through the work of the 'readers' of the books who spent time and patience reading aloud for cassette and DVD recordings for those who were denied by failing eyesight the pleasure of tucking up in bed with a good book.

We are not short of high profile courageous women today. In the newspapers and on television one proud determined woman fought for the right of Welsh women to be given the cancer drug Herceptin, taking on the might of Government and winning...

In signing off I would like to congratulate the contributors to all three anthologies; not only for their high quality literary ability but also for giving of their time so generously. It makes me proud to have my roots deep into the fabric of this place we call Swansea.

(This story of The Misses Angels and Their Farm was also published in Courage and Ambition, as it shows the courage, the determination and strength of these two sisters. Yet, the story also conveys the ambition of the Misses Angels, namely the ambition to see justice done. – The Editor)

The Story of the Misses Angels and Their Farm
From an account by E.E. Rowse, written in 1896.

It was in the autumn of 1890 that I found myself one glorious afternoon, accompanied by two congenial companions, parading the Mumbles Beach and enjoying with them the many extraordinary views, which the clearness of the atmosphere revealed to us. The light of the sun burnished the tops of the distant hills, and we could see in the distance the frowning heights of Craig Lynn and the towering cones and ridges of the Afan and Rhondda Valleys.

We saw the white cliffs of the Nash rising out of the sea, and Dunraven Castle hard by, looking like a sentinel and guardian of the land on duty. The whole coast-line was well defined by the golden sand dunes, which abound all round the foreshore. A large number of trawlers were still afloat and the numerous skiffs and pleasure boats which skimmed across the bay in graceful attitude, made up a sight never to be forgot.

Calling for a boat, an old sea salt, on the look-out, struck a bargain with us, and after a few minutes rowing we found ourselves far out in the bay, just under Mumbles Head.

We soon found the old salt very agreeable and full of traditional stories, which he related to us quite freely, and of which the following is the substance:

'I remember the Mumbles for the last 70 years. I am in my 79th year. I consider the sea has encroached nearly 100 yards since I was a boy, as the stumps and the roots of trees along the shore testify. I know all about the Misses Angels. There were two sisters, one of whom was blind for a long time.

They lived in yonder house close to the shore (the first house after leaving Norton for Swansea) and during the winter, when the waves rolled over the protecting wall and threatened its destruction, they would move down to the Ship Hotel and remain there until the winter was over. One of the sisters lived in Angel Street, Swansea, in the house now known as the York Hotel, and died there. This was 30 years ago.

It used to be told among the fishermen that the Angel family would become extinct. There used to live in the parish three families – the Robins, the Madocks and the Angels. Each of these families opposed the laying down of a tessellated pavement in the church, whereas the other parishioners were desirous that this should be done.

They heaped curses upon the heads of those who opposed the scheme, and swore that they were accursed, and that their posterity would become extinct. And this actually happened, as we have no Angels, nor Robins, nor Madocks left.

I have seen the maps and ancient pictures which prove that a large extent of land, now submerged in the Bay and extending as far as the Green Grounds, formerly belonged to the Angel family.

When Sir John Morris' father wished to work a quarry in the Mumbles Hill, the Misses Angels insisted that he should pay them so much for 'way leave', but this old Sir John stoutly refused to do. The Misses Angels determined, however, to defend their rights and the case was tried at Carmarthen Assizes. After long contention, the judge expressed his dissatisfaction with the proofs of ownership, and the Misses Angels were mulcted in costs.

However, they were not to be turned aside from their purpose, so they employed a barrister and had the case tried at Hereford, and here again the case seemed to be going against the maiden ladies. It happened that the counsel for the defendants had been detained on the high road, and that, consequently, their case proceeded without him. Fortunately, however, he arrived before the conclusion and, after apologising to the judge, he was allowed to cross-question the ladies.

This elucidated many facts, which had been withheld, and as the old documents were produced in court, which proved that all the lands in the neighbourhood of the church as far out as the Green Grounds, belonged to the Angels, the jury were convinced. The judge gave them a verdict, which ultimately ruined Sir John Morris and caused him to leave the country.

The plan of this ancient property showed distinctly a farm-house, where the sea now covers the Green Grounds. Also a large meadow, which was crossed by a country stile: but all this has long ago disappeared and the very memory of its existence lingers only in the minds of the very aged. It appears that the public records of the reign of Edward IV speak of the great floods, which devastated Glamorgan, and this tremendous storm continued for several days.

But the most extraordinary flood recorded took place in the early part of the reign of James I when an Atlantic tidal wave swept up the channel scouring both coasts and doing fearful damage. It overwhelmed Grove Island, the farm and the meadowlands on it effacing forever almost all traces of its exact whereabouts. However, it is well known by means of an old map, that it was not far from Mumbles rocks and that it occupied the site now known as the Green Grounds.

I am getting an old man now, but I can remember my grandfather speaking of the traditions which his ancestors handed down about the ancient wood, known as 'The Silver Wood' and how it gradually disappeared, and what I heard has often been confirmed during my life time. I remember some of our men fishing up the hors of an antelope, the ox and the stag and recovering tusks of the wild boar.

I have oftentimes heard also the tale of the last boar that was killed at Norton. How it was forcing its passage down one of the long lanes leading to the shore, but it was speared by a spit, which killed it on the spot, and this is why the natives call the lane Boar-spit Lane to this day.'

Thanking the old salt for his interesting stories as we landed, we bade him farewell and then made our way to Swansea.

Previously published in the Mumbles and Gower News, February 1970.

http://www.themumblesbook.com/history/themissesangels.htm
18 May 2004

Gwen Bailey

Blessings (In what things do I know Him)

You knew and loved me before I was,
Called and found me in a darkened hour.

Showed me where to look each day,
How to ask and what to say.
Filled me with Your Spirit's breath,
Brought me life and banished death.

Recognised in goodness
And the blessings all around,
That's the joy of feeling
You are always to be found.

Promises in rainbows,
Strength and power in sea,
Warmth and light in sunshine –
Showing You to me.

Children and relations
All precious in Your sight.
Taking care and loving them.
Making all things right.

Friends and lovely places
Glowing with Your love.
Like sparkling stars and candle flames,
All blessings from above.

Thank You, dear Lord Jesus,
My Husband and my Friend.
I worship and adore You
And love You to the end.

Connie Bewen
Blessings of Water

In the Old Testament God hovers over the primeval waters and brings forth the world from the infinite Ocean. It is a motif echoed in creation myths throughout the world. In each, water is the fundamental precondition of life.

Scientists tell us that ice floats when most solids sink, and why, being highly corrosive, water is good for us.

But how do we, as people, view this H_2O?
The *Maid of the Mist* is a small ship that glides slowly past a frightening torrent of water known as Niagara Falls. To be near that heavy flow is awe-inspiring beyond belief. One feels the terrifying power of the water, attempts to understand how this power is used and, in our world so obsessed with appliances and gadgets, suddenly appreciates that such wonders exist.

The *Queen Mary* is a large ship that acknowledges the majesty of a vast expanse of water called The Atlantic Ocean, three thousand miles across and a thousand fathoms deep.

To stand on the prow of that huge vessel is to witness the rapid changes of mood exhibited by the sea: the fury of that water, its violence and its gentle calm, what it has done to the many who have been trapped by its treachery, what it has contributed to the many who have sailed over its peaceful shining water to a new and joyful life.

Yet the extent that *Water* remains a scientific mystery is extraordinary, despite its prevalence and central importance on the earth.

Glynis Buckham
Worlds meet and spin

Today's drizzle leaves rain
holding tight to cobwebs
hanging between trees.
Silent watchers,
they guide us
through this misty evening
to the Cathedral.
Inside it is warm and softly lit,
spice- rich incense burns,
a drift of jasmine
meets the scent of candle wax
Musicians enter, take their place.
People settle. For a moment,
silence steals a heartbeat,
then the playing starts.
The roof curves down,
reaches towards the music,
finds the rhythm
from other worlds.
 A memory of Spain lingers
a chant, a dance,
sounds of mourning from Greece,
a dedication from France.
Next the evening call to prayer.
Worlds meet and spin,
flames grow, passion flickers.
Racing through the cloisters
a bat emerges,
casts a brief shadow on the altar
and vanishes.
The Cantigas continue
telling of miracles.

Malcolm Bullough

My Blessing
Upon Swansea City Centre Bus-Station

Imprisoned space,
stagnant,
old,
no longer hollering to cast-off your chains:

may the night-stars glimmer on your broken head,
and the dew of the dawn anoint your desolate floor.

Maureen Chapman
Blessings in Disguise

Proverbs 10:22
The blessing of the Lord, it maketh rich
and he addeth no sorrow with it (A.V.)

The blessing of the Lord brings wealth
and he brings no trouble with it. (N.I.V.)

For those of us who have a bumpy ride through life, and that probably includes most of us, it is often difficult to see where or how we are blessed by God. More often or not we feel buffeted and bruised, even traumatised, stumbling blindly through difficulties, hoping fervently that somewhere, somehow, we have got something right. Probably deep down, we hope that we haven't made such a mess of ourselves that

God has decided to abandon us. Are we a waste of time and effort on His part?

Verses such as this one in Proverbs seem to bear no relation to ourselves. This is especially so when we find ourselves facing yet another difficult situation. How can we cope? It's too much to bear.
How can life, or God be so cruel?

We need to realise that this verse is not for the chosen few who swan through life with a permanent heavenly smile on their faces. It is for people like us.

God's blessing will make us rich, wealthy and there will be no trouble, no sorrow mixed in with it, here and now, in this difficult place we find ourselves in. The richness or wealth does not refer to money. It refers to the benefits of being blessed by God.

We can be blessed with peace, made rich with a peace that is beyond understanding in the most stressful, bumpy of places. We can be made rich in love, flowing to us from God and those around us, and flowing out of us to others. God himself is Love and in his presence there is no bitterness and no fear. Nothing can happen to us except what is allowed by Him, and filtered through his love. Thus there can be no sorrow, no trouble for us, whatever the suffering, whatever the outcome, whatever deep scars remain.

In perfect love, there is no fear. What a priceless gift, to face life's traumatic difficulties without being paralysed by fear? With fear comes self-pity, rebellion, a kicking against events, a desire for revenge, a deep destroying anger and jealousy, a 'why me?' attitude. Here we find relentless sorrow, and much trouble. No wonder people turn to drugs or alcohol or anything that will blot out all memory.

How sad this is, when all our resources are to be found in God. In accepting the blessings God has made available for us, we can find all that we need to cope with life's bumpy rides. These difficult, painful times can become places of blessing enriching us. There will be scars, emotional, physical, mental, but they will not have the power to restrict us, to disturb our peace, to paralyse us with fear. Instead they will be powerful reminders of the way God has blessed us and made us rich.

Alice Cook
Blessings

Hi, my name is Alice. I live in Gorseinon, Swansea. I am 12 years old and go to Penyrheol Comprehensive.

I guess that blessings are just things that make me feel happy and special, and lots of things do that!

Like my friends. They are really kind and helpful and always cheer me up when I'm down!

Winnie, my Jack Russell, makes me happy too. She makes everyone laugh and point and say "awww!" She is really mad but that's why I love her!

Also my parents are great too! They spoil me and cheer me up. Sometimes they're embarrassing but I'll forgive them!

I love going on holidays too. It's just really peaceful and relaxing and no one knows you so you can be your self. My favourite holiday was Florida. I swam with dolphins!!

Going to theme parks makes me extremely happy! I have to go on all the rides because I know I'll regret it if I don't.

Just knowing that I have more than some people and that I should be thankful is a blessing!

Ann Cooke
A Day in the Life

Fallen asleep over my book, the rising Full Moon, orange and mysterious, called me to wakefulness at 2am. It felt like a blessing. I moved my pillows to the foot of the bed and moon-bathed to sleep again. Four hours later the debates of sparrows and the playfulness of seagulls lured me to consciousness. "Wake up and join this glorious day!" they insisted.

Obeying the birds, I went to the kitchen, which greeted me with a celebration of sunlight and the clean, fresh smell of the sea.

The Sparrow Family, chattering on the phone wire, brought me to the window where I noticed that a miracle had happened in the night. The taller of the two potted sunflowers had begun to poke, tentatively, some of its yellow petals out of the egg of its bud. Maybe the birds had seen it too and were calling me to share the joy of it. With a bit of patience, my kitchen would soon be blessed with two radiant sunflowers.

I sat in the window with my cup of tea, reading my book and enjoying the warmth of the sun. Something made me lift my eyes to the Bay where a magical sight was begging to be noticed. A large three-masted sailing ship was motoring its way at a stately pace into the harbour.

My first thought was "Pirate Ship!" sneaking in on the tide before most of the town were awake enough to notice, for that's what it looked like from here. My sense of wonder at the beauty of the graceful barque rig was contrasted with a mild feeling of alarm and danger. Could this have been a memory from the days when my Celtic ancestors lived in terror of invaders from the sea? Or an echo from the Norse side of my family excited about the plunder they would amass on this journey?

Overcome with curiosity, and the binoculars being inadequate to help me see exactly what it was and why it should be making its way into Swansea Harbour, I set off on foot to the beach where, near the old Slip Bridge, I pointed myself in the direction of the Marina.

Walking, walking, enjoying the sun on my legs and the sensation of moving in lightweight and light-coloured clothing, I came off the beach at Marine Walk and strolled into the Maritime Quarter, admiring the yachts and other vessels bobbing at their moorings.

Walking, walking, there was no sign of my ship, so I kept going and found myself on the Sail Bridge. From there I could see the three masts with their tell-tale cross-pieces standing proud over the rooftops of some pre-fabricated boatsheds.

Walking, walking, through a wasteland with not another soul or a spot of shade in sight, I eventually found myself passing through a gate beside a freshwater pond where seagulls and ducks were splashing and drinking happily. These were the only living creatures I'd encountered for about a mile, but the verge was dense with wildflowers of every imaginable hue, including rogue rapeseed plants emitting a heady scent of honey. Around the corner of a warehouse, there she was, the *Tenacious*.

I had to screw up my courage to walk past the signs that said NO ADMITTANCE WITHOUT HARDHAT & HIGH

VISIBILITY CLOTHING so that I could read her name on the bow. I could see some people on deck who were not wearing such protective gear, so I marched on in. After walking all those miles I was not going to be deterred at this stage from getting close enough to examine her properly!

A friendly young man was hosing down the decks. He accepted my compliments about her beauty and told me the *Tenacious* belongs to the Jubilee Sailing Trust, a charity based in Southampton, which offers people with disabilities the opportunity to experience the wonder of sailing on the high seas. She would be sailing out of Swansea in a few days, and he said he would ask the skipper to raise the mainsail so I could watch her from my window in the Uplands.

I enjoyed the walk back to town, stopping on the bridge to watch a school of mullet in the river and pass the time of day with a workman in a hardhat. At first he looked as if he was playing Pooh Sticks, which would have been very appropriate on this spot. He told me of the habits of mullet, scavengers that help clean up the nasty bits in the water.

Practising saying "Ta-Da", I left him happily watching the fish and made my way to Sainsbury's. There I picked up a takeaway salad, which I carried into the town centre via York Street and consumed in the grounds of St Mary's Church.

Walking, walking through the Market I was tempted by the cherries and some lovely cheeses, including a Chèvre and a locally made strong cheddar.

Heading for Wilkinson's, a gypsy accosted me – "Never turn a gypsy away, dear" - and gave me two glass pebbles, blue and red, to hold in my hand while she tried to read me. A man is desperately in love with me, I have suffered in marriage, I have found happiness at last here in Swansea . . . all the usual stuff. For the "lucky pebbles" she wanted £5(!), but she took pity on me when I showed her my empty purse and told her I was a widow. She let me have the blue one for 50p; the advice was for free. You can buy a kilo of these pebbles in PoundLand. I wonder if she makes a good living from her enterprise.

I am not ashamed to confess that I am having a love affair with Swansea. It woos me like a lover and I respond with passionate devotion. The little discoveries I make on my walks are a constant source of delight. Just climb to the top of Constitution Hill and look back at the view. And all is for free.

Noticing and celebrating the little things – a seagull coughing up a greedy lump of hamburger that went down the wrong way, a tiny purple flower growing out of a stone wall, cuttlefish littering the beach, the lights around the Bay on a clear night, the sighing of the trees in a gentle breeze, the smell of the sea, the friendliness of strangers – is a spiritual discipline, a positive affirmation of the privilege of just being alive and having all one's senses intact.

The capacity to enjoy the simple pleasures of life is inherent in each of us, a gift from our Maker. My prayer for all is that we shall never be so overcome with cares that the little blessings abounding in each day are overlooked.

Lilian V. Davies
Snowflake

Scanning the universe
Seeking eternally
A twin, a clone
Each humble snowflake
Creation of genius
Bedecked, bejewelled
Studding and sparkling with diamonds
Arms geometrically perfect
Branching with secret tracery
Unique under a microscope
A star of wonder
Queen of design, exciting, prime
Swirling in a blinding snowstorm
Silently in some exotic dance
Softly, slowly until in embrace
With a trillion million stars
Falls to rest in a blanket of rime
A miracle of transformation
A world shot from black to white
In a night, peering through
The dark the starlight sings
Across the sky

Margaret Davies
I Count My Blessings

My husband died - very suddenly and unexpectedly – in June 1999. I am not a naturally gregarious person and had always hidden behind him so had to make a conscious decision not to stay at home and vegetate.

Since then, I have been blessed in many ways. My granddaughter was born in April 1999. My son, Graham, has brought her to visit me regularly and she introduced me as a 'reader' in the local school.

My daughter, Helen, lived in London. I visited her on several occasions and we were able to go together to museums and concerts. Now, she has returned to Cardiff. We go to plays and, because she sings with a choir, I have been to concerts in Cardiff once again.

Holidays abroad have always been important. After the death of my husband I went to Italy, alone. Since then, my sister has come with me - or vice versa – to Iceland, Norway, Finland (and several places between) and to Glasgow for my Australian grandson's christening.

My daughter, Helen, came with me to Australia to visit my son and his family. Add to this the friends who have introduced me to the WI and Probus and a neighbour with whom I have been on various art and craft courses- most importantly, woodcarving - and you will understand why I count my blessings.

Gillian Drake
The Botanical Gardens, Singleton Park

A beautiful garden is a blessing, and I am lucky in that I have one close by which I can visit at any time. This garden is not mine; I am not responsible for its upkeep, and that is part of its attraction. For some, the labour of creating such a space full of growing things is a blessing in itself, but I have never been that way inclined and so for me the joy is redoubled: without having had to lift a spade or pull up a weed or lug a lawnmower around, I can immerse myself in all the peace and quiet and colour and fragrance of a garden whose constantly-changing display of plants reflects the seasons from spring through to winter.

On this warm day in July, I sit outside in the shade of a large tree, enjoying the perfume of sweet peas and the clean, medicinal scent of marigolds; and watch the orange and yellow globes of some flower whose name I don't know floating on their slender stems like colourful butterflies.

If I do want to discover the names of these horticultural delights I can find them out with ease, as all the plants are considerately labelled – but today I prefer just to sit and admire them. No need to know what they are in order to do that!

In front of me is a living Impressionist painting of people at leisure in a garden landscape of smudgy pinks and blues and yellows streaked with delphiniums (I know what those are without looking) in azure and sapphire and lavender blue to co-ordinate with the sky.

The picture is framed with dark green trees and bordered with a shingle path, and in the foreground there are freshly mown lawns still glistening from a recent shower of rain.

It is restful here - so close to the heart of the city but you wouldn't know it - there are trees and walls to surround and seclude; the sound of water from a fountain to soothe and distract from the troubled thoughts; and a gentle breeze tumbling through the leaves overhead. A child runs, briefly, across the grass, chasing his own shadow.

A burst of laughter floats over the hedge. Goldfish laze about in ponds, squirrels lope, alert but relaxed, in the hope of bits of food, and bees go about their business in the flowers, oblivious to all the cares of the human world. Nobody is much bothered about things here, and that is as it should be on a warm summer's day.

When I have rested for a while and am feeling more energetic, I can go and look at the vegetables. These are an altogether more workmanlike proposition, occupying a space of their own that shows that they mean business. Away from the flowers and the grass and the rows of wooden benches, they display their orderly lines of greenery in the shade - crinkled parsley, frondy carrot tops, the leaves of beet - red-veined, wrinkled and tough, as I shall be if I hang about too long in this sun - and curly lettuces.

Between them the earth lies brown and level, with little insects hurrying about in it. This is the working part of the garden and it is just as pleasant, in its way, to look at, as the flowerbeds. One can almost feel the roots expanding under the earth; cabbages heartening out under cover of their big protecting leaves; potatoes shoving each other aside to make more room for their ever-expanding tubers; carrots spindling determinedly down, and lettuces whooshing airily up.

There are herbs, too, and these I love, for they seem to me to occupy a position midway between flowers and vegetables: scented, medicinal, and edible.

They do not look very prepossessing at first glance, seeming duller and weedier than flowers, and less robust than the lusty bruisers of the vegetable garden; but they do have a muted and delicate beauty of their own. Sometimes, when you have been looking at herbs, flowers seem overstated and you have to adjust again to taking in all that colour and scent.

Herbs evoke everyday homely history – bringing to mind the houses they have freshened, fevers cured and stews flavoured – and the gardens scented and cooled by their soothing presence down the centuries. From the manor house still-room to the humblest cottage garden, herbs have found their way into peoples' lives from the time when the first Neanderthal experimentally uprooted some hardy wort or greenstuff in his chunky fist and, in a moment of inspiration, threw it into the fire with his haunch of mammoth and discovered, say, rosemary or mint sauce. Yes, herbs definitely rate as a blessing.

I end my tour of the botanical garden with a stroll up through the walled garden, its plant-packed borders backed with warm and sheltering red brick. All along the way are numerous wooden seats, inscribed by loving friends and relatives in remembrance of people now gone who loved this garden: those who have passed through here and have shared in the enjoyment of the place over the years. As I walk past their memorials on my way to the gate, I am filled with hope that they are indeed resting in peace - and enjoying the blessing of a garden for eternity.

Ruth Ellen
Blessings: Mothers

As village children we were used to turning up at the vicarage. It was partly our house anyway as we had staked our territory in the rooms when it was being built. Sitting in the kitchen we'd be fed home made biscuits and ginger beer. The source of the ginger beer was under the stairs in a dark cupboard, some 'growth' for the next batch, alien and a bit creepy to me at the time. Scones were made on the griddle, a soft mixture dropped onto the hotplate, flipped over and placed on the table for our casual consumption.

This hospitality was on an unspoken understanding that we would do something useful. Today it's to make posters for the jumble sale with colourful lettering. Last week Carol and I made a map of the graveyard, a plan of the whole site, every grave in its place. It was an accurate map. I've often wondered why they didn't have one and if ours made the archives. There were many graves without headstones, two of them my own grandparents. Were my relatives so poor that they couldn't afford to mark the grave? It's a question I never asked my father in case it upset him. There's still an aunt of ninetyfive.

Should I ask her or would that be unkind? Does it matter? I heard a Hindu man talking on the radio last week explaining their custom of sending their loved ones into the next world at the end of their life, life afterwards for relatives to be used for the future. Should we have graves at all? I dreaded the thought of my father lying in a grave, but now I do find it a comfort, it means he's not entirely gone. There is no right way, obviously. Anyway, as children, we'd noticed there were many unmarked graves and felt a bit sad for the people below.

It's strange how attending church was part of childhood but it's something I left behind once I moved away from the village. It may have been something to do with belonging or a commitment to others. Undoubtedly it involved worrying about God being neglected. Since there were only four of us in the choir it would also have involved feeling the vicar was unsupported in his mission of caring for us all if we didn't turn up. He'd be there on his own and we owed it to him to join in as we clearly benefited as a village from him and his wife, particularly his wife. My recollection is that she provided us with constant reassurance that we all belonged, no question about that, and made sure we and our families had outings, celebrations, holidays and other treats such as Simnel Cake at the end of Easter service and Easter egg hunts in their garden.

Children congregated at regular intervals in her kitchen, joined her 'Kings Messengers' club, put on plays for the village and ran stalls at the annual fete. On these visits I'd often slip into the garage to visit the rocking horse, riding for hours on this handsome wooden friend.

I've lasting memories of the vicar's wife digging the garden, cooking, organising a party game or laying out a picnic on the steep sided field above the village. Meanwhile our own mothers were taken for granted, my mother hand sewing my school dresses, buying me spike shoes for athletics, thrilling to the sound of choir singing at open days, setting me off into the world with brimming self confidence.

Blessed memories? I think so.
For some reason I have had a fairly long series of relationships without settling into marriage and family life of my own. This brought relationships with other mothers, the natural addition to the son, my partner. Each seemed unconditionally supportive and congenial which makes me feel they have earned a position in warm or blessed memories. I was allowed entry into the worlds of other families, for me, a bit like moving around an advent calendar, into and out of the windows of the private and cherished life of others.

If you stay with one partner the picture record can be built up like a photograph album and memories shared between the two. Moving on means letting go, relationships lost but also something retained and gained. I hold my memories together, along with others who have been alongside throughout and that's fine. Visions of these relationships filter through my mind like silent summer movies, bringing light and laughter, pictures with muted sound as if flickering on a blank wall. I wonder why they are easier to remember than sad times?

I remember a moment in my thirties, in 1981, during a cold spell in Holland, a frozen scene by lake Islemere. At minus twenty degrees, my boyfriend Alf and I walked over frozen peaks, waves caught in mid air. The ice creaked. As we crossed

the expanse I looked back to the shore as I'd done six months before in the summer from our boat. We were walking on water. Would we become a headline in tomorrow's paper, drowned, if we didn't get back there soon? Reassured by him we covered a mile and returned. Later, from land, I saw across the fields fresh faced couples and children as they raced and glided on a network of canals, the wonder of Holland, waterways lacing beside roads, each crossing the other. From the winter sun people collapsed into cafes and sat by the fire with a warm drink before heading home.

Alf's mother provided the focal point for the family, with her husband, rescued by her in the war. I find myself on a sofa with her, watching a super eight film, pictures taken in Australia in the sixties. Having emigrated along with many others to the land of plenty, they spent twenty years raising their family of three in the sunshine. She is on a swing in the garden, confident and waving, laughing as usual. She is eclipsing the sparkling sun as she swings to and fro across the screen, larger than life with a buoyant mannerism which she continued to spread on her family and me.

Ten years before, in Oxford, I had spent some time with Janusz, my first long term partner met at a party he'd gate crashed when I was nineteen. His parents lived on the Eastern edge of the city spires. We visited often and after his father died I lived there for a while whilst I still worked as a nurse in the city. Janusz' mother kept house for her Polish husband, a man who had fled to England during the war, having seen his grandparents thrown down a well by Russian soldiers. Without his papers he had to take work on the line in a car factory. Their life introduced me to the companionship of male Polish friends. In a fug of smoke in the small English sitting room they'd tell tales of near miss tragedies and homeland. The budgie looked on and, starry eyed from the smoke, brushed up on the language.

As a primary school teacher, Janusz' mother radiated authority as a professional woman, sharing her frustration about lack of resources for the needy children and scornful of unnecessary bureaucracy which delayed the most obvious action needed for vulnerable children. She was concerned when a small boy had spent the whole day on an outing in rubber boots because he'd outgrown his shoes; and when newly qualified teachers were not taught how to manage a classroom of children and she would be called in to keep order.

It added up to a world drifting without common sense for her but one in which she took part and played a balanced role of give and take. She did not take on the world's problems. She was committed to the children and her work but she and her husband also took for granted their right to relaxation and pay back.

Long school holidays, timed with the annual closure of the car factory for worker holidays meant coach trips abroad to Spain or France. To me, at twenty one, I took my hat off to them for heading off in such a casual way on cross continental trips, they seemed a bit old to be doing that sort of thing but I realise now they were only in their forties. Some years later, aged forty nine, Janusz' father died from lung cancer. A carriage clock, acquired from the thousands of cigarettes purchased stood testament to the cause. Smoking was taken for granted in the seventies and warnings subject to argument and hard advertising. I missed him. I enjoyed his company and the acceptance I had as a member of the family. It was sad he had his life cut short. Overall, though, it was a lovely time in my life. There had been many lovely people and times in my life.

My parents did not have the money for experience of travelling abroad for holidays at all. I found myself with growing opportunities in life as others lived it yet with anxiety about my parents not getting their fair share of fun. I was living a blessed life, yet somewhere a voice questioned my right to such fortune. We do not exist in a vacuum.

There are always others around less fortunate. Does that spoil the pleasure? Hard to tell. They may be more fortunate in other ways. I learn it is not helpful to think of others as victims or to be in a rescuer role. Unless there is obvious disparity. Personal autonomy brings a sense of self and self worth. My parents for example had five children and I know they were proud of each one.

My mother in particular says she enjoyed those days when we were growing and she the homemaker and they both continued to bask in the trials, tribulations and pleasures of growing grandchildren. It is therefore not necessarily a good thing to be too preoccupied or sad about my perceived needs of others.

We have a short time on this earth we have entered. Some are luckier than others in the opportunities for life and development.

We know of vast differences in cultures, religion, war and peace across the world. There appears, to me, to be a need for mankind to manage the fundamental rights of individuals in the best way they know how. I am the product of my upbringing, family and society, and therefore see it as I have been programmed to do and understand through observation and reflection.

Others come from their beginnings and perspective. Although one species we are not coming from the same place once our first breath is taken. Genetics and environmental influences are not fully understood but the sciences allow us to partly see the real differences their influences have. However, not many seem to want to hear or understand those difficulties but want others to be like them. World peace is an almost unattainable goal. Starting at home may help.

I feel I have been very fortunate and from the start have had the advantage of growing and working in a life which has provided love and has opened up an increased understanding through work, research and education. I could envy the lives of others for their growing families or continued relationships with partners I have had to leave behind but I don't.

I cherish all memories but I have learnt by example and practice that life offers changing challenges. These maintain in me a wonder and unquenched desire for the moment. Belonging to a time and culture that is taking a shared responsibility for the wellbeing of mankind provides me with a means of joining in but also leaves me with space for the sheer joy of living.

Ruth Ellen
Blessing: Love of Life

Salt Lake City sun, real live music playing and I've stopped for a beer at the Mountain Stag Café. I can see for miles across the Rockie Mountains. The sky is cobalt blue, trees green and the snow is soft and easy. I think of my father and how I used to think of him whenever I was savouring a life he had never known. My love of nature, voice and rhythm comes from him.

When I knew there was a chance to write an article on *Blessings*, I thought of my father and the way 'bless' is used in Swansea, the way my mind flies past pictures of him as a child, with flat cap, by his hatted mother in a charabanc, waiting for a village outing to the sea; an unmarried man, seated in trilby hat and smart shirt sleeves, looking out to sea; as a father on Weymouth beach making sandcastles, pipe in mouth or the one with him proudly facing the camera displaying '1st Prize' fruits from the flower show.

There's also a favourite, a photograph my sister has, of him in his eighties, in bed, too thin but laughing, wearing a newly acquired Australian hat recently brought back from a trip by his grandson. I'm listening to the morning birds at 6 am as we leave the hospital. Dad has been left behind on his bed and won't be coming home again this time. He died a few hours ago. I felt sure he would see through another night, but how could he. He was so weak and thin.

The birds sing sweetly in the fresh sunlight on this cold January day. It's as if they sing for him. He loved birds, spent hours watching them, feeding them from the table or by hand. Swallow nests were protected by making sure we didn't play near them and hedges were left to grow high for their nests. That's just as well as, in general, fields are expanded, hedges removed and chemicals sprayed.

Birdsong always lifts my spirit. Birds are up so early, reminding neighbours they also live on earth with their own territory. Their lives are shorter but with bursts of energy in the warm sunrays or on a fresh morning they have an enormous effect on the turning world.

Wrapped up in Dad's world was a life of felt poverty, feelings that he had not achieved anything and also harsh words for some members of the family and society in general. He told me in his last months that he felt disdain from his parents-in-law when he married their daughter. Our family relationships with all extended families were close and friendly but there seemed some acknowledgement that we were a large family and that somehow that was not quite as presentable as smaller, better financed ones, all this somehow Dad's fault. Since we've grown I have discovered that these same cousins did not hold those opinions but looked on us with envy for the companionship of brothers and sisters, playmates and soul mates.

It's amazing how convinced we can be about others' views when in fact they are only personal fears. Who knows what is real and what imagined. I discover it is best to assume the most positive scenario because it sometimes seems to be able to bring about that state.

The youngest, bar one, of five children himself, Dad grew up just after the First World War. A recently found photograph finds him standing, aged five, apart from his classroom mates, in an over sized coat and grey socks. It's his first term at school and he has an anxious look. There is a gap between him and his three older siblings who are together in the back row. Look at him. He looks lost. Don't you just want to take his hand and say it's all right!

On his first day in school he managed to lose his one and only pencil, having poked it through a hole in the floorboards. No doubt he was given another but he marked it as measure of how firm and authoritarian school life had been for him, when talking to grandchildren who were experiencing the huge opportunities available to them in current times.

Aged eighty five he found and retrieved the same pencil when the school was converted into a house. Belonging to the village was very important to him. I imagine it gave an unquestioned order to life, childhood, marriage, children, provider, retirement, dying with honour. In later years, as many elderly people are, he was preoccupied with memories of childhood, for him his mother, her cooking, times from the war, village boys who never returned and his lost years of careless youth.

Memories were tinged with guilt. He never fought on the front line and told me that although the war had taken his youth he hadn't done enough, conscious of others who had lost their lives. Thanks to hard work and endurance of my mother, his wife, he was eventually comforted by spending his last few months in the same room and place his mother had died, where he wanted to be.

Aged twelve years, he was sent to work as a 'hand' in a manor house, forty miles away. He'd left a newly acquired dog at home but found his mother had given it away as soon as he left home. It was too costly to feed it. This was not unusual. Children had

to work, we know, to feed working class families. He worked six days a week and a half-day on Sundays. Rising at six o'clock he'd set and light the fires and act as general help in the kitchen and garden. In later years he could keep us entertained for hours on past experiences but the tales from this period were brief. He had been very unhappy in the house and ran away on the pretext of going to the dentist. He was a man of honour with a strong sense of duty so I believe there were hidden reasons for his rapid departure. He clearly had a strong dislike for the head gardener.

For the rest of his teenage years and after the Second World War, he worked on a local farm and for a builder, where he learnt a variety of building skills. He made friends of other tradesmen who later worked with him on contracts which required several skills. He became self-employed as a painter and decorator. This was the father we knew.

Meanwhile, the Second World War had enlisted him and other young and hardy men and women in six years' service. Unfortunately, during training in Scotland, he had slipped from a ladder and injured his back, which ended in an operation to fuse lumber vertebrae and caused limited flexibility and chronic pain. Although, in his work as a decorator he produced first class work, he always thought of himself as not quite good enough - and undercharged. Working for farmers and landed gentry he would however bring home extras such as pheasants and other game, given as gift for good service.

Fortunately, he had married a young girl who had a very good head for finance, management and love and sense of duty for the family. His small income, added to the harvest from his kitchen garden, provided all meals and daily requirements. My parents were house owners too, having rejected the idea of living in a council house. My mother had saved money from pre-marriage years, so we were property owners too, all of this taken for granted by me.

Life in the village, with his growing family, was sustained and lively. It ran around the routines of weekday work, evening gardening and drinks, darts and card games in the pub at weekends, an interest in sport, especially football. An annual fete or flower show provided a framework for shared fun and an edge for careful gardeners who could compete for recognition of their skills and achievements. The world of the pub changed, of course, through the years.

As he grew older, the village pub opened up to women and then, horror on horrors, started serving food and acting as a popular restaurant for neighbouring visitors. There seems to be nothing quite as territorial as a West Country village. Men like my father had to readjust rapidly in their maturing years to developing society. Their years of sacrifice and duty given to the country was paling into the past and youngsters showed little concern for the life chances the older villagers had foregone.

Thank goodness for memories of endless stories, his delighted pleasure in outings in later life. We seemed more visible to him in his last year. Goodbyes came with a hug and he'd say he loved us. Years before we have first prizes in flower shows, any number of trips to gather mushrooms for breakfast, hazelnuts for Christmas or a chain of apple pickers in the autumn, carefully handling the cooking apples, our staple for Sunday lunch. Perfect specimens were kept for festive seasons. Dad planted, we reaped. That was the deal.

When he died, two years ago, the village church was full to overflowing with people who wanted to be there for him and for us as a family. He had not always acted in the most favourable way and in later years could be very critical of almost anything. Nevertheless, he had a great presence and managed to hold an audience, share his awe of nature, enthuse over exchange with life through trips out or telling tales.

The money given at his final service was used for a safety handrail in the tower, from ground to first floor, where the bells are rung. It proved handy quite soon afterwards during an electrical storm when all lights went out leaving the bell ringers stranded. He would have been very pleased about that. A plaque was placed on the door leading to the tower in his memory.

The live café music plays on, but the sun, more weak, is going down. It casts long shadows from people who are making their last ski trip to the bottom. I need to join them and arrive at the base to slip into the end of day happenings with my partner and his children. I take with me the blessings from my father's memories, inner strength he has given me and my love of life.

Caroline Gill
Beside the Swansea Sea
Tracing the Footsteps of Frances Ridley Havergal
(1836-1879)

The Mumbles Lighthouse caught my eye, as I took in the wide sweep of Swansea Bay. It was 1992, and I was captivated by the fluorescent buoys, the coils of rusty rope and the sound of the sea. I soon discovered the delights of the Gower Peninsula, with its fine churches and hidden coves. On one occasion, I came across a plaque, commemorating the nineteenth century poet and hymn writer, Frances Ridley Havergal.

In my mind's eye, I picture Frances in the last year of her life, scurrying along by the water's edge with her unmarried sister, Maria. Jesus had called James and his brother, John, to be *'fishers of men'* beside the Sea of Galilee; and here beside the sea in Swansea, God was calling the Havergal sisters to continue their Christian work.

Frances and Maria had moved to the southern edge of the Gower coast, between Bishopston Valley and Caswell Bay, after the death of their stepmother in 1878. Frances had soon settled happily into what she called her *'quiet little nest'*.

If I walk towards the Mumbles pier on a summer evening, I find myself zig-zagging in and out of a tangle of fishing rods, while families wait patiently for a bite on the line. I smell salt in the spray, and imagine Frances stopping to exchange a word or two with the fishermen's wives, before she started for home.

Maria recalls how her sister studied the Nautical Almanac, in order to understand about the safe navigation of ships, and the vagaries of weather and tide. Frances became acquainted with the Mumbles Lighthouse Keeper, and enjoyed asking him about the workings of his light.

Sadly, Frances caught a chill, and died from complications some days later, on 3 June 1879. The words on the plaque outside the Havergal sisters' Gower home are as follows: *'She being dead, yet speaketh'*. Hymns like *'Who is on the Lord's side?'* and *'Take my life, and let it be consecrated, Lord, to thee'* are still sung all over the world, with much *hwyl* today. The great preacher, Charles Haddon Spurgeon, referred to Frances as *'the last and loveliest of our modern poets'*.

As I peer out towards the Mumbles Lighthouse from my window high above the bay, I think of Frances and the many blessings she counted, as her Swansea days flowed *'in ceaseless praise'* for Christ, her Lord and Saviour.

Caroline Gill
Blessings of Unity
Inspired by Psalm 133

Lofty mountains rise to meet us,
shining with the morning dew;
showing that our Lord will greet us,
lead us on to pastures new.

We will walk the way together,
with each step in unity;
with our God and with each other,
Heaven's gate our destiny.

We shall pass through raging waters,
with our Father as our guide;
for he loves his sons and daughters,
and his arms are open wide.

Let us join with all creation
as we soar on eagle's wings:
we will tell of God's salvation,
share the peace his Spirit brings.

We must run the race set for us
with the cross before our eyes,
for Christ's death and resurrection
show a love that never dies.

Caroline Gill
St Govan's Chapel: Blessings of Faith

The south-west wind blows in on rolling waves
while gannets gather on the weathered rock:
their voices echo through the sea-swept caves.

A grey seal surfaces and seagulls flock
towards the cliff as raging seas run high.
Who built this hidden chapel, block by block?

Its walls declare, beneath a brooding sky,
that God created sea and sand and stone,
and out of love he sent his Son to die.

Christ's tomb was sealed: God's saving work was done.
The third day dawned: the stone was rolled away.
When women came, they found their Lord was gone.

He was alive - indeed, he lives today:
this wave-washed chapel, hidden by the tide,
calls us to turn to Christ, to watch and pray.

We scan the sea and know our God will guide,
for Jesus stills the storm, and Jesus saves:
we grasp his hand, as cares are cast aside.
The south-west wind blows in on rolling waves;
a grey seal surfaces and seagulls flock.
Our voices echo through those sea-swept caves,
as we proclaim that Jesus is our rock.

Jennifer Gray
BLESS(INGS)
DICTIONARY QUOTATIONS,
ETYMOLOGICAL CONUNDRUMS

Bletsian, bledsian,
Northumbrian bloedsian,
Old English blothisojan [1]
Mark with blood
Sprinkle the blood
Onto pagan altars
Bledsung, bledsung [2]

'No cognates in other languages' [3]

No?

X1c.blecier, [4] *blyési,* [5]
Recevoir une blessure… [6]
'Wound me' says the olive
'Make me grow sweet and soft'.

'On faire une entaille:
On obtient ces sucs
en blessant les plantes.' [7]

Bruise the plants, soften their flesh
For the feast
Measure out the pinioned
and cruelly extended branches
Along the whitening wall.

★ ★ ★

The wounding, the blessing,
The blood,
Mingling and merging in
An etymological swirl
Recall another wounding, bruising,
Blessing.

1. To consecrate, make holy, to mark with blood (Old English).
2. Blessing (Old English)
3. Online etymology Dictionary
4. To bruise – of fruit, to make sweet (xi c.French)
5. To soften (of fruit) (la Suisse romand)
6. Receive a wound (French)
7. One makes a cut, and obtains juice by wounding the plants.

Monika Henkler
Welsh Blessings

The beginning of my story dates back to the year 1978. At that time my favourite uncle asked me whether I could accompany him on a trip to Canada. He wanted to visit relatives who had emigrated there in the sixties. But as he did not understand nor spoke a single word of English, he feared problems regarding communication.

In those days we lived in a small village consisting of five hundred souls in a rural area in the middle of Germany. I was thirteen years old and had learned English at school for three years, more or less reluctantly. If one wanted to see the 'big wide world' in those days one simply drove by car either to the North Sea or to the Alps – at the most to Italy. A flight to Canada was outside my imagination then – but it was a challenge!

To cut a long story short: we managed reasonably with my English in Canada. The stay of four weeks in the East of Canada did not only expand my view of the world as such but also kindled my interest for other cultures and languages. I therefore also studied English for nine, Latin for five and French for two years as well as some Spanish with ever growing enthusiasm. It may seem incredible to some readers of this book but I really did not know till my visit to North America that English was a universal language and that one could conduct conversation *purely* in that language *and* understand it.

After I obtained my A-levels in English, I took the plunge to move from the countryside to a big city and studied in Berlin. I then joined the Foreign Department of the Department of Work and Pension in Berlin. There I learned a great deal about the life in the most diverse regions of the world and also practised my knowledge of foreign languages, particularly English.

Six years ago I found myself in South Wales, for private reasons. Suddenly, my good – had I imagined it to be good? – knowledge of the English language did not measure up in comparison to the spoken English of the locals. I also found that daily life was very much different from Berlin. Life in Berlin and Wales was a different matter, two very different lives indeed. Everybody knows those British TV-sketches where the 'typical' German shouts 'No time! No time!' and hastily runs away. Instead of which I now heard statements such as 'I'll do it sometime!' or the local saying 'I'll do it now in a minute!' – which used to drive me up the wall!

But, meanwhile I had to accept a compromise regarding two different ways of life. Life in Germany is so very much more pressurised, one simply cannot get away from hectic or *('über'-)* correctness or seriousness. Life in Wales taught me to be *more* tolerant, to be *more* relaxed and to be *more* open towards my fellow human beings and situations in general, private or professional - in short: to think/live outside the box.

As far as language is concerned: My English is fluent now even if I have to admit that some people call it 'Wenglish'. I regard the comments on my Welsh English as a compliment. English spoken with a German accent sounds ghastly to my German ears – whereas I consider 'Wenglish' a much better option!

After three and a half years in Wales I have returned to Berlin and taken up my former job. I remember my time in Wales with fondness. Even though I have travelled widely in the intervening years and have met people of the most diverse habits and customs I must say that I have retained a soft spot for the Welsh. One of their most outstanding characteristics is their warm hospitality.

There is simply nothing more relaxing than downing a pint in a *cwtshy* lounge of a local pub in the company of friends and neighbours. I must also say that I never have been met with such unbiased attitude (despite the often mentioned *Blitzkrieg* in the tabloids). On the contrary, I have always been welcomed with openness and hospitality. In Wales I have come to know a 'different world' which gave me not only lots of different experiences but lifelong friends - yet it taught me so very much about myself into the bargain.

In retrospect I must say that my journey to Canada in 1978 was a blessing as it awoke in me an interest in the English language but also the curiosity of life in 'the big wide world'. Without this interest I would not work in my present job which gives me such joy. I would never have moved to such a big city as Berlin, would never have lived abroad (definitely not in Wales) and would not have had the pleasure I experienced there – nor would I have met such good Welsh friends.

And who knows what the future holds for me? But one thing is certain: my knowledge of the English language and my newly won Welsh openness and relaxed attitude will be a great asset to me.

Epilogue:
Somebody whose mother tongue is the English language has a huge advantage over someone who has to learn it as a foreign language. I am sure that not many people are aware of this – which is a great pity!

Jenny Impey
Recounting

My dream is of the Gower blue sky
Neath high white clouds sighing idly by
And then I see in the dappled light
Of a stream myself in the fancied light

Of a book well loved and nearly done
So I feel like a stretch and crave for a run
Over Rhossili Down from South to North
With the hang gliders up and soaring forth

And once I have danced on the wave crest foam
I climb the sheep path on to Burry Holme
And gaze at the porpoises schooling around
By the light that once guarded the estuary sound

If the abbey were more than a ruin again
I imagine I'd stay and forever remain
With the peace of the thought and the labour and prayer
Of a group of quiet people industrious here

But the light it is changing, black clouds scudding by
And I notice the storm in the West bids me fly
Away up the hill, over dunes and across
The green moor of St Cen with its rain-sodden moss.

Elsewhere the rain drops as a vertical fall
But the curtain out here horizontally squalls
As I turn round to front up the oncoming drench
I raise up my face, close my eyes, feel the wrench

As I'm swept off my feet and carried on high
Like a leaf in the fall I seemingly fly
And my heart is so full of the fun and the joy
Of the freedom of being, just tossed like a toy.
Then from flying above and soaring aloft
I'm floating to earth, deposited soft
In the sand of the beach, in the bay by the dock
And I come to myself and awaken with shock

As I see that so far I have mused for an hour
In my fantasies wide over glorious Gower
But I need something else, it won't do on your own,
That your blessings are less if you number alone.

I must seek out and share them with those who would fain
See the blessings redouble as we count them again.
So of all, quite the beset is the swell in the breast
As you're done with the roam and must now cut for home.

Around Dylan's Square	With the old anchor there
Along Sketty pill	And up Killay Hill
As you head for the West	Over Fairwood crest
And down toward	Cartersford

And your heart centre knows that you're nigh the repose
Of a soul that is blessed and a body at rest
In the heart of your family, friends old and new
You can work with and play with and cherish them too.

Betty Jones
Blessings

When I first considered the invitation to write about blessings, my thoughts went back to my schooldays and Morning Assembly, when – most to my surprise, now – so many of the hymns emphasised the theme 'blessed'.

Like me, I am sure that many of you will remember singing 'Blessed Assurance', 'Blessed Jesus meek and mild', 'Blest be the tie that binds', 'Blest are the pure in heart' and so many more to be found in *Hymns and Service for Schools* or in the glorious *Book of Common Prayer* (reign of Queen Elizabeth I) with its *Hymns Ancient and Modern* – such a treasury of wonderful inspiring words. That, of course, was followed in the early 17th Century by the King James Bible with its beautiful language.

Amongst our books at home there is a concordance of the Scripture which gives considerable space to the Welsh word 'Bendeth' (Blessing) and takes us on a journey which shows how, from Genesis through the Psalms to the *Epistles* of Paul, there is evidence of God's care for his people. This is specially marked in *Deuteronomy*, chapter 33, where the emphasis is on the *Blessings of the Tribes* led by Moses.

Lest I should be accused of being sanctimonious, I will remind myself that it is not only from Christian teaching that one gets such guidance and inspiration. Literature is full of references to *blessings*. Surely we all remember (having learnt it by heart!) Portia's *Quality of Mercy* speech when Shakespeare stresses that mercy is

'...*twice bless'd, It blesseth him that gives and him that takes.*'

Izaak Walton, the 17th Century writer, tells us in his
Compleat Angler:
'...*health is the second blessing that we mortals*
are capable of; a blessing that money cannot buy.'

It would be good for us as a conclusion to consider Wordsworth's words in his *Tintern Abbey* when he inspires us with these thoughts:
'... *nor all*
The dreary intercourse of daily life,
Shall e'er prevail against us, or disturb
Our cheerful faith, that all which we behold
Is full of blessings.'

Pauline Lewis
Count your Blessings

There's dust upon the furniture,

Stains where the paint should be,
But I must count this blessing,

That I have eyes that see.
There's a roar of passing traffic,

Strident voices drawing near,
I count this too a blessing

That I have ears that hear.
There are flinty paths of suffering,

Barbed words that make us reel
But we will count this blessing

That we have a heart to feel
And we're filling up your suffering

Who died upon the tree
And we thank you for each pain you bore
That we might be set free.
Thank you for hue of rainbow,

Glint of pollen on a bee
And thank you too, when sight should fail

Yet still by faith we'll see
The glory of your kingdom

And the beauty of your face
And how can we count the blessings
Of your amazing grace?

Our ears may lose their sharpness

Yet we still will hear your voice
And feel your touch of gentleness

To cause us to rejoice.
How can we count the blessings

Of the gift of each new day
Bird song and clouds and sweet fresh air

As we press on our way
And grace, love and forgiveness,

Heavenly life that will not end
And though earth's joys may pass away

You're still our faithful Friend?

Alan McNally
Blessings of Children

There is a verse in Psalm 127 that speaks of the blessings of having children. *'Children are a heritage from the Lord'* it says, *'Happy is the man who has his quiver full of them'*. In my own experience I have found children to be a mixed blessing. Great when you are having fun, or on holiday, but a bit of a problem when you are intent on getting on with something and they are demanding your attention. As an aspiring writer I have found them to be a useful source for material.

I started telling children's stories because my first child wanted tales about subjects he had chosen, rather than from the books we had bought him. However, finding the time, and quiet, to write them down later, with a lively youngster trying to get involved with everything I was doing, was a bit of a trial. Just like now, as I am writing this, my four year old grand daughter Katie is distracting me with her questions, and demonstrations of the many different ways she can fall off the arm of the couch in my study.

A man I once knew, much older than I at the time, told me that children increase in value as you and they grow older. I fondly dreamt of mine as an investment as they grew up. However, I was brought sharply down to earth, finding the teenage years a virtual stock market disaster as they deprived us of our hard earned cash with their sartorial excesses and hare brained schemes! Then, suddenly, they were up and gone, travelling the world, only phoning home now and again when money got short.

How my wife and I boasted of their newest exploits and yet secretly longed again for those early times when we could put them to bed and know exactly where they were. Then there were the girlfriend/boyfriend years of tears and traumas, mixed with joy and excitement, which quickly changed to marriage and grandchildren.

A settled existence at last. I suppose the psalmist knew a thing or two after all, but why a '*quiver full?*' Quivers have arrows in them; they are for shooting..... aren't they? It was a joint birthday party for my 21 year old youngest son, and my one year old first grandson, that started me thinking.

Had my wife and I been given, in our children, a quiver full of arrows to polish and sharpen and shoot into the future? Arrows, that would make a mark in the world, thirty, sixty, one hundred years from now, passing on our ways, thoughts and aspirations to a world that is to come, allowing us to influence days we will never see, in some small or great way, was this the blessings that the Psalmist had in view?

I was reminded of another scripture, this time from Isaiah 44, '*But now listen, O Jacob, my servant, Israel whom, I have chosen. This is what the Lord says, He who made you, who formed you in the womb, and who will help you: Do not be afraid, O Jacob, my servant, Jeshurun whom I have chosen. For I will pour water on the thirsty land, and streams on the dry ground; I will pour out my Spirit on your offspring, and my blessing on your descendants. They will spring up like grass in a meadow, like poplar trees by flowing streams.'* I can say a hearty 'Amen' to that! Looking down through the years to come, the thought of my children, grandchildren, great grandchildren and their children's children being blessed, and being a blessing, fills me with joy.

Mavis Morgan
Blessings

On Friday 22nd of June 1990 at 9.55pm my life ended. A telephone call from a surgeon had told me I had breast cancer. Withdrawing into a bubble of disbelief, isolation and turmoil I knew this was the end. There was no way to escape from this dark and endless tunnel of despair and fear.

Alone when the phone call came I had to break the news to my husband when he arrived home from an event in the local school. He had taken my place at an evening I had organized as I was recovering from the removal of a supposed benign lump.

Next day I had to decide on which treatment I wanted and the following Monday I was operated on in the care of wonderful nursing and medical staff. My husband and children were so supportive as were my many friends who visited me in the ward. But they hadn't had cancer – they had no idea what it felt like to have a death sentence hanging over their head. It was like a bereavement and I spent my time reassuring everyone else that I was fine – it was the only way I could cope with their concern.

By chance, my husband was due for a dental appointment with a good friend of ours and he produced a life line for us. He knew of a lady who had been through the same trauma as I and would ask her to ring me. Thus I was introduced to someone who would become a dear friend. I went along to her group and I could not understand why these ladies were so happy! They all had cancer for goodness sake but some were many years away from diagnosis.

These ladies gave me something I dared not think about previously – hope. With their help I began to believe there was life after cancer and after a long time I was able to think "OK, if I only have a short time left what a waste it would be to cry it away". But if that was not the case I was wasting a second chance in life. My mortality had been brought home to me and I was given the opportunity to live again.

Neighbours and friends were still supporting me as my husband's work took him away for months at a time and once I had grown stronger he reluctantly returned to sea. I shall never forget the family who would turn up weekly with mowers and spades to do the gardening along with their young child.

As time went on, our daughter who had been in the middle of her A-levels during my trauma but nevertheless passed her examinations, went off to university. Our son who was only 8 in 1990 was my biggest concern – would I see him through school?

Sixteen years later I still count my blessings - our daughter is happy with a partner and as a social worker. We have seen our son graduating from university and starting a research post.

My husband has retired and we both enjoy time together and help others in our voluntary work. In the intervening years we both have been involved with other cancer patients and their partners and served on many committees helping to change the services for all cancer patients.

Life is good and we appreciate we are the lucky ones and wish to dedicate this to all our special friends who have enriched our lives but are no longer with us.

Liz Morrison
A Bed of Roses

Do I really want my life to be a bed of roses?

Or would I just wake up complaining about the thorns that sometimes hurt me, moan to you that the petals are not as beautiful as last year, the stems not as strong, or the dew not as wet?

Maybe awaking to miracles could happen everyday, but people find the light of them too bright, the shock of them too much, or have too much darkness in their life to light their view. Perhaps I would see more miracles with a little more faith and a little more light in my life.

Thank you for the others who have chosen to share their life with me, and stand by me through the sunshine and storms. Thank you that I do not have to go it alone, and others, warmed by the sun of my bright days and battered by the winds of my storms, have committed themselves to being my blessing.

As I go through life, I ask that I will not be so blind as to not notice the homeless man, the widow, the orphan, or the victim.

Thank you that I am a blessing when I use my mouth to smile at a stranger. I have been a stranger and when another smiles at me, I know at least one other person out there is on my side.

I am a blessing when I use my hands to feed someone who is hungry. I imagine that if they are that hungry they will eat anything.

I am a blessing when I use my voice to freely give praise. I know what it is like to hear encouragement amid hopeless despair.

I am a blessing when I use my ears and eyes to actually listen. When a friend or stranger needs to let someone know what is burdening their heart, and the only silent language they can use is the everyday.

Help me show others that they too can be a blessing, when they offer anything they may have, however small or big. Then maybe one day we might all wake up in a bed of roses...

Lauren Murphy
What makes me Happy

My name is Lauren Murphy, I am twelve years old (turning thirteen in December). I have lived in Asia, North America and Europe. I have been to Australia and snorkelled in the Barrier Reef when I was four. I love to play Soccer, I used to play Softball in Canada but I took up Soccer instead.

I am also learning to play the piano. I love to go on holiday and I love animals; my favourite animal is a Polar Bear. I also love colourful things, my favourite colours are neongreen and pink. I love to go snowboarding, especially in the Canadian Rockies, I love to hang out with my friends in town or go to a movie and I love to sing and act. I love my family, that's what makes me happy.

I am very lucky I have been blessed with a healthy family. My immediate family is Ian (Dad), Samantha (Mum), Caitlin (sister 10 yrs) and Imogen (sister 4 yrs). Though sometimes they are a drag and also very annoying, they make me happy. They make you laugh and they comfort you when you're sad. My family makes me happy because we are so close, we tell each other everything and they can tell when someone is upset and we talk about whatever is bothering us. We almost always have a family dinner.

Though we have different interests we always find something to talk about. I don't like some of the things Dad likes and I certainly don't like some of the things Caitlin likes that's why we argue sometimes. My family makes me happy because they cheer you up when you are sad and most of the time they don't make you sad. Children that have unfortunately lost their

parents or siblings find happiness somewhere else; there is happiness all over the world.

I love it when your parents or Guardians take you on holiday, because you are spending all your time with them. Another thing that makes me really happy is when we (my family and occasionally a friend or two) all watch a film together.

I find happiness in my family because they are also there for you just like your very close friends. Your friends are a bit like your family because they hate it when you are sad, so they cheer you up just like your family. Sometimes your friends are so close that people think that they are sisters.

You spend about 1/4 of the day with your family and about1/2 of the day with your friends (at school); you're almost always talking to them on MSN as well! That does vary on weekends and whether you are at a sleepover. I love being at a sleepover, it makes me really happy because you are doing what you and your friends love to do. It's really nice when you have a sleepover that is really girly.

Another thing I love to do and really makes me happy is going shopping. Any girl my age loves it, we all love to go together and can't wait until we finish school for the holidays so we can go all day!

We all have been given the opportunity to live, and you only live once, you have some good times and some bad times, and we should all strive to live our lives to the fullest but most importantly the happiest way we can. I have gone to school in three different continents – it's been a great opportunity but I have moved away from my friends and family and I didn't feel great about it, but you have got to move on and think about the opportunities and not dwell in the past.

Carole Pearson
The Gift

Flowers are a gift from God
For sure you will agree
They transform a dreary garden
Of mediocrity

Into a place of splendour
Somewhere we can share
Thoughts ideas and troubles
Or talk to God in prayer

Wild flowers fill our meadows
Dancing in the breeze
Decorate the hedgerows
And crowd beneath the trees

Our world became a better place
The day flowers God invented
Each bloom he moulded perfectly
Each one he slightly scented

Then with a splash of colour
To match his rainbow bright
Some he painted vividly
Some he left pure white

Next he made the seasons
A time for each of them to grow
Little snowdrops in the wintertime
Peeking through the snow

Daffodils in springtime
Golden trumpets shining bright
Little birds returning
From their winter flight

In summertime Geraniums
Mauves and pinks and reds
Fill our tubs and baskets
Adorn the flower beds

But in the fall the Dahlia
Stands tall in misty rain
Glowing through the autumn months
Too soon, it's winter time again

So, on your journey through the years
Allow flowers to impart
Colour and fragrance to brighten each day
They surely will gladden your heart

And if you feel sad and blue
Because sunshine has turned into showers
Just remember it's because of rain
We have

THE GIFT OF FLOWERS

Paulette Pelosi
The Water in my Blood

I didn't need to tippie-toe a white
Welsh-wintered digit into the warm water
To know…
I already *knew.*
I didn't depend on a nanny-state travel guide
To dip a calloused elbow in to test the water
To know…
I'd known a *long* time.
I had bathed, splashed, waded and wallowed in
The waters of La Rava
Through generations.
When my father made his return journey
To his Comino valley, I was the Maremma
Closely sniffing at his heels.
When he rolled his Welsh-bought, denim-sort
Trouser-legs, introducing septuagenarian limbs
To latest generation Italia tadpoles
I followed.
Us, two generations of the Ciociaria
Who had 'gone to Wales.'
The wine chilled beneath the surface,
Bottled sacrificial bubbles for our communion
As the bells of Sant'Anna tolled the Angelus.
The hot sun holy suggested siesta but this mad dog
Stayed out and sniffed the air for family.
I took a big breath in of my Pa, Luigi,
As then a boy from Vallegrande
Splashing with his friends in heady, undiluted joy.
There was Nonna Carmela, skirts hitched, bravely
Risking passage through swollen depths,

Nonno Giuseppe, the boys, Dominic, Tommaso, Loreto,
My aunts, Angelina, Teresa, Nina, Dora, Gloria…
And my dear Godmother, Carmina – 'Kim',
Setting a rosary of stories to bless my steps.
Piacere La Rava,
Always in my blood.★

★Paulette wrote in explanation of her poem:
'All my life, my dear Papa had richly described to me tales of long boyhood summers in this area – and his treasured moments swimming in La Rava river…

I wrote the poem in 1999. It expresses my exhilaration at discovering, for myself, the magic of this river. My first visit was indeed with my father, on his return journey to that area of Italy, after an absence of sixty years. His magical memories and the reality matched perfectly.

I wore a simple cotton dress. I found a fallen branch to use as a stick to support me. I walked in that river, water levels much lower in summer… and I experienced… BLISS. Each year that we were able to return (with our picnic of freshly-cooked pasta in a cooking pot and a bottle of Asti Spumante to share) I felt the same… like years and any strain had been lifted off my shoulders… I felt the same feeling of BLISS! The shape of the poem with its alternating lengths of lines, for me, represents the meandering path of the river…
My Papa died here, in Swansea, in 2001 – four months from diagnosis to death with prostate cancer. The poem stands as a memorial to his strong spirit'.

Liz Porter
My Grandfather's Blessings

Thomas Grufydd Meyrick always counted his blessings. One of his favourite hymns which he used to pound out on the piano was 'Count Your Blessings One by One'.

He was born in September 1886 at Taillywd Road, Neath Abbey. Listening to family oral history, he probably inherited his get-up-and-go from his mother Annie Elias who, although she could only sign her name and manage basic numeracy, owned and ran the village shop. His father was an 'invalid' who spent a lot of time in bed. Today he would possibly be known as an alcoholic. There was one other child of the marriage, a girl named Roshanna.

Thomas Grufydd Meyrick (always known by the full title) left school at the age of twelve because he wrote a good essay called 'How Tom Belled the Cat', and he passed the numeracy test. The brighter children left school first or earlier having passed the school leaving test.

His first job was looking after the pit ponies. He loved this job. When he was a little older he became a miner.

He was ambitious and went to college to gain the qualifications to become a fireman in the mine at Cefn Coed, Neath. Firemen were the first men down to check for danger and the last men out when there was danger.

The job was synonymous with danger and, inevitably, there were accidents. The year before he was due to retire Thomas Grufydd Meyrick was involved in an accident. He saved the life of a young miner but his own right leg was crushed so badly that he needed to have it amputated. This did not deter Thomas Grufydd Meyrick from living a rich and active life right up to the ripe old age of 89.

Much earlier in his life there had also been personal tragedy when his one son was killed in the Second World War. His four daughters lived long and happy lives. His wife never really recovered from losing her only son, and I remember her as just always sitting quietly in the fireside chair.

When he had recovered from the trauma of the accident in the mine, Thomas Grufydd Meyrick embarked on living 'the Third Age'.He had many friends. Tuesday was his chess day. He had been a Deacon in the Welsh Baptist Chapel. He loved to read and to play the piano, self taught. He kept the most magnificent garden which ran down to the brook, one of the tributaries of the River Neath.

He considered himself well off because he grew all his own vegetables and kept chickens. Because of his accident he had free coal for life. He counted all these as Blessings. Thomas Grufydd Meyrick was my maternal grandfather – and a hero.

Louise Rigdon
Blessings

When I was approached to write this article I was asked to write about 'blessings'. And really it made me think because I have never seen my life or the way that I have lived it as a 'blessing' I have just always seen it as me being a fortunate person!

I graduated as a Primary School teacher in 1999, and I have been fortunate to use those skills teaching in three different countries in the world. My first teaching appointment was in Bucharest, Romania. I remember old footage of the fall of Communism, those terrible pictures coming from orphanages, and so this experience felt more like a living history for me. It was a bit like asking your Gran what it was like living during the war.

I had seen the television coverage, and I was able to ask people, young people my age, what it was like living and growing up under a Communist regime. For me, it was amazing to hear young people recalling having their first *Kinder Egg, Coca Cola,* banana or orange. For me it was an incredible experience living in a post communist country, still struggling to get back on its feet, but with a determination to try to succeed!

In saying that, Romania is a far from ideal or perfect country. There was poverty, terribly poor people, whose daily lives were such a struggle that is too difficult to describe or even to imagine. Through a very good friend, I was fortunate to be introduced to a couple who worked for the City of Hope charity, who had ten street children living with them.

This young couple had totally handed their lives over to God and to the children. Their house, despite being incredibly busy, noisy and chaotic at times was so full of love. This house and family were what I would have classed as 'blessed'. To find love and security in such difficult circumstances is surely a blessing.

I was also fortunate to work in the Cayman Islands in the Caribbean. Here, amongst the sand and constant sun, I was able to learn what was important to me. Being so far away from home makes you think about the important things in life such as family and friends.

I was very fortunate to make wonderful friends, friends who I could share everything with, who have kept in contact, who would be there for me through anything.

I also had a lot of time to think about my family. I have been very lucky to have had such a supportive family who have encouraged me in every adventure I have undertaken. During this time in Cayman I realised how much I needed to be close to them, and I decided to return to the UK.

However, as things were starting to settle down for me in Swansea, a teaching job in Alexandria, Egypt came my way. I have always wanted to go to Egypt, and with my travels I have found that you discover far more about a place when you live there.

I don't believe that I was ever prepared for Egypt. It is a busy, hectic, noisy, dusty country. The concept of being a passenger in a car in the country is terrifying to watch, or even worse, to be in! Maybe it was travelling through the roads in Cairo at break neck speed that I started counting my blessings! If it was, then I certainly wasn't aware of it at that time!

The thing that worried me most was the religion. As a country we have been watching the troubles around the world, the 'war on terror'. We have been taught through the television and by politicians that the religion of Islam means the religion of the Terrorist. I was worried about going out due to the July bombings in Sharm El Sheik, and due to the fact that I am an open Christian. I even left my cross at home. I really didn't know what to expect. I remember waking up on the first morning a little after 4am to the sound of the Sheiks in the city calling people to prayer.

It is a wonderful time of day in Alexandria – the city is at its quietest, with the eerie, almost tuneful sound rippling through the areas in the city. I loved this time of day, to hear people of faith being called to worship God. I was also very lucky to live in a building that was completely lived in by the same family. They welcomed me with open arms and I was totally adopted by the Arafat family.

They accepted me, my traditions, my faith and my opinions, just as I accepted theirs. I sent Christmas cards; they sent Ramadan cards. I invited them to a Shrove Tuesday party; they invited me to their Eid celebrations. We often had discussions about faith, and it was good to openly discuss with them ideas from the west about Islam, and to learn first hand, what Islam is about. My Egyptian family are good Muslims who are not terrorists. They are loving, kind, wonderful people, who loved me as much as I loved them for their ideas and views.

So, how have I been blessed? I have been blessed to have the opportunity to live in three very different countries. I have been blessed to experience three very different religions – Christianity, Orthodox Christians and Islam. I have been blessed to be loved by a wonderful family who have always supported me. I have been blessed to have found such wonderful friends who will always be there for me. I have been blessed to teach 62 children from every walk of life, colour and creed in my career. Looking back, I can see how I have been incredibly lucky, fortunate, and very blessed!

Irene Roberts
My Story

When I was asked to write something for this publication my immediate reaction was to pass it on to someone else. As I'm not one to express my emotions easily, but then I gave it some thought, and having read some of the stories in the other two publications I felt I really must give it a try. So here goes!

I was born in April 1947, the youngest of four sisters – my childhood was not what I would regard as happy – as we sadly lost our mother at the age of 27, my eldest sister was only 10 years old and I was 18 months. As you can imagine, it must have been such a sad occasion especially for my older sisters realising that our mother had gone to Heaven. Not wanting to go into too much detail the family was in turmoil. Fortunately, we all managed to stay together for a number of years. This is my story of Blessings.

Much of my younger life had very little stability and purpose – no parents to guide me through my childhood or adolescence I desperately wanted to be successful at school and believed that I too could achieve something one day. I failed my eleven plus but was successful in attaining a place at Gorseinon College onto a Secretarial course. This gave me the opportunity to get an office job, where I could work and progress through a career.

I got married very young, at the age of 19 years. My husband and I celebrated our Ruby Wedding this March – and we have two wonderful children with a gap of 13 years between them. It has been my joy and inspiration through life to watch them grow and mature into beautiful adults and has indeed been the most wonderful gift that I could ever have had.

My daughter has been my friend and confidante. We have shared such wonderful times together as she was growing up with lots of fun and laughter and now she has become a wonderful mother to three beautiful daughters who are the greatest gift to us all.

My son, born 13 years later than my daughter, has also given my husband and I such pleasure and as a young enthusiastic sportsman has made us proud on many occasions with his successful achievements as a young schoolboy. He has yet to find his right partner in life, but I'm sure there will be someone special for him also, as he too has grown into a loving caring person who lives life to the full but always knows his roots.

My life has not been without sadness and I do feel I missed what I regard as the most important time of anyone's life as a happy childhood, but I can thank God that I have made up for that loss in the three people that have made me so very happy – my husband my daughter and my son, and now, of course, my three gorgeous grand-daughters who we absolutely adore.

I do thank God daily for my Blessings.

Walford Roberts
Jesus, Redeemer, Lord
Tune: Bethany

Jesus, Redeemer, Lord,
Draw us to Thee;
Tho' tir'd and weary Lord,
You yet spoke to me.

'Come friend to heal the sick,
Tend to the poor and blind;
If you will lose your life
Peace with me you'll find.'

Megis â Iacob Fawr
Ym Methel gynt,
Ti Dduw a ddaeth I mi
Er na'th welais Di.

Ond yn dy gariad mawr
Fry yn y nef a'r llawr
Engyl y ne' yn llu
Cydiais ynof fi.

You saved the Magdalene
From stonéd death,
Then gave her life anew
With a priceless wealth.

Her tears are yours and mine
Sin's power crushed and gone,
Cleansed in the blood of Christ

By His Vict'ry won.

The Welsh words recall Jacob's experience at Bethel, and remind us that God is always with us, even when we are unaware of His presence.

This is believed to be the first bilingual hymn in Wales.

Jean Salkilld
Summer Gold

Long, light days of summer
Soft warm breezes,
Golden sun

Long, light days of summer
Perfumed roses,
Golden lilies.

Long, light days of summer
Busy bees,
Golden honey.

Long, light days of summer
Seaside visits,
Golden sand.

Long, light days of summer
Luscious strawberries,
Golden plums.

Long, light days of summer
Country harvest,
Golden grain.

Jean Salkilld
Finding Contentment

As I sit in this café and stretch my eyes across the bay, I am looking at a view that has been familiar to me all my life. The café is always congenial and friendly and there is always a place at one of the small, round tables. On arrival, there is the up-beat welcome: 'Table for two, madam?' and the inevitable answer: 'Please, near the window if possible.'

Today, the bay is set in varied shades of grey, from the dark grey of settlements clustered around its great arc to the shining silver-grey brightness of its water. Small areas of trees and yellow threads of sand appear here and there, backed by low-lying hills. There is a clarity about this grey day, that emphasises the vivid blueness of a lonely small boat and the eye-catching orange of some scattered buoys as they lull themselves on the gently receding tide.

I have seen this bay in all its moods and colours, in its calmness and storminess and in its uncertainty. There have been the sunny days that reflect onto the blue water, the burning sunsets that cast it into red and gold and there have been the unusual blue yellow skies that reflect into a green sea. But, whatever its mood and colour, I only see the familiarity of it all, the stability of the natural scenery around me and the extending view across the Bristol Channel.

Today, the café is comparable with a beehive, buzzing with spirited chatter and activity. The cold chill in the air and the Easter school holiday have conspired to squeeze many people into this sheltered place, where we can enjoy ourselves, yet pretend to be out in the healthy fresh air.

Two menus are available in this café. There is the one that gives the choice of looking around for familiar faces accompanied by friendly chatter, smiling at children, reading the daily newspapers provided, watching the activity around the bay or, perhaps, just nourishing a moment of relaxation.

There is the second menu that can only be described as pure enjoyment and today, the eager demands and statements of all ages filter through the air:
'Can I have a Pizza Margherita, Mam?'
'I want a strawberry sundae! No, I want to change that. I want a raspberry sundae instead!'
'Make up your mind, Daniel!'
I settle for a latte and a kiwi sundae and all is well in the world!

There is a feeling of freedom about the bay, open to wide expanses of sea and sky, that appears to belong to no-one and yet belongs to everyone. We are free to throw caution to those who will be bound by it, to bathe in its summer moodiness or play rounders in its winter rain. And who should be concerned when we curl a long tongue around the chocolate sauce flowing down our ice-cream cone?

There is always movement around the bay. Occasionally, my view is interrupted by groups of intrepid walkers, wrapped up against the chilly weather or a cyclist in circumnavigation mode or a young couple strolling hand in hand or a father with his child on his shoulders. I have fun trying to identify the varied breeds of dogs taking their owners for a walk. In the distance there are tiny people chasing a ball on the beach and a lonely figure walking along the tide's reach. Everyone appears content to have something to do, even if they are doing nothing:

"The wife and I enjoy sitting here, just watching, watching..." We tend to retain and revitalise memories when they encapsulate our happiest experiences and I declare my guilt in doing this when I reminisce to family and friends and, perhaps, bore them into polite acceptance of those happy days on the "Sands" near the "Slip" and the rides on the old Mumbles Train, that rocked us from side to side from Rutland Street to the Mumbles Pier. Sometimes I catch the interested tourist. Some things have been lost, I say, and some things gained on the way to updating the environs of the bay. But this is the present and its natural beauty is still the same

As I begin to read today's newspaper headlines and absorb the café's ambience of well-being once again, I glance, now and then across the bay. I know that this is where I want to be. So, I order another latte and nourish the moment.

Sister Marian, S.C.L.
Blessings Meditations

When I was young,
I was blessed

Because my family brought me to God.
When I was a teenager
I was blessed

Because God called me to serve Him.
When I grew up
I was blessed

Because God gave me an aim in life.
When I faced rejection
I was blessed

Because God showed me He was in control.
When I was working
I was blessed

Because God developed unknown skills .
When I was married
I was blessed

Because God showed me I am loveable!
When I was bereaved
I was blessed

Because God gave me strength to go on.
When I became ill,
I was blessed

Because God took control of my life.
When I am in pain
 then I am blessed

Because I have a share in the cross.
When I have to rely on others,
Then I am blessed

Because I learn humility.
When I have to let go of so much,
Then I am blessed

Because now I have more of God.
When I die
I will be blessed

Because I am going home!

AMEN

Carol Smith
Precious Blessings

Blessings are precious – they are gifts from God. There is a song that says *Count your blessings, count them one by one...*and we have so many things to be thankful for. The first thing that I am thankful for is my husband. It says in the Bible it is not right for man to live alone and husband and wife are joined together by God. My husband displays the love of God in his love to his family and his generous and loving heart. My husband has demonstrated this time and time again and this was specifically emphasised last year.

I had finished work and was commencing the Christmas holidays. It was the first Monday off and I was going to a Primary School to prepare a Christingle service with the children. It was such a beautiful day, the sun was shining and everything seemed so perfect. My husband was home because he was unwell and I said farewell to him and got into my car.

On the way to the school I went to pick up my friend and I noticed that the sun was particularly strong so much so that on one part of the journey I was completely blinded. I said to myself 'I hope I'm going to be all right'. As I proceeded on the journey, I overtook a parked car and the sun blinded me and as I drove on I hit a bus head on. I could not even grasp what had happened to me.

My car was wedged in the bus and I was looking up at the bus driver and I could not believe that I was still alive, unhurt. I had not even felt the impact when I hit the bus. Two young girls asked me was I all right and I said yes and I was dazed and standing around as the shock started to set in. The road was completely blocked and I removed my car from the bus and parked it at the side of the road. All the occupants on the bus were unhurt.

I started to search in my bag for my mobile phone. My son answered and got my husband. I told him what happened and he was there in minutes. He placed me in the car and I cried and I felt God said *Because this accident happened you shall have a new car.* By the time I arrived home, the insurance company had decided to write off my car. I still could not believe that at one point I was driving along the road and the next I was involved in a major accident! I realise that I could have been killed and this experience highlights the gift of life and how very precious it is.

Two days later I looked for a new car and the sales advisor gave us a test drive and before I could say *Jack Robinson* we bought the car and completed all the paperwork. The sales advisor said 'Somebody up there must like you as normally the tax disc would not be available until after Christmas but the car is registered now and will be available on Christmas Eve.'

I was so excited that I could not sleep. Within two days I was sitting in my new car thanking the Lord for my husband who supports me and makes sure that everything is in order. I also thanked the Lord who protected me and saved my life. What a blessing. Thank you, Lord!

Ceri Thomas
Blessings Are

Blessings are a gift
that serve without question
and heal a broken soul.
A candle that guides you in the dark
and the gentle hand that lifts you, if ever you should fall.
Standing silently beside you – waiting for you to call.

A life without blessings is as stark
as a darkened maze. Burdened and weary,
dragging life behind you for the rest of your days.
Never seeing beyond the walls
of your airtight shell.
Suffocated by the isolation of your self-made cell.

And time will pass by
as quickly as the thoughts in your head.
Shedding tears for the life you never lived
and what you could have had instead.
If only you had opened your heart to the joy
that life can bring.
The silence that had cruelly pinned
you down could finally learn to sing.

Blessings are a gift
that serve without question
and heal a broken soul.
A candle that guides you in the dark
and the gentle hand that lifts you, if ever you should fall.
Standing silently beside you – waiting for you to call.

Judy A. B. Thomas
For You*

You have had a disappointment, my brave beloved friend
But hold on fast to your faith, for this is not the end
It is just the in-between time when things are not quite right
And fear becomes embracing like the darkness in the night
But I will be there to help you, so put your hand in mine
Together we will be strengthened by a power that is Divine
We will not allow our tears to cover up a smile
And if you should feel weary, I will let you rest awhile.

Perhaps you will feel angry and ask the question: Why?
Let me take your anger, together we will cry
But in the quieter moments I will offer prayers for you
That God in His great mercy will grant you health anew
I have no gift of healing, simply am your friend
But through this precious bond, myself to you I lend
When your cross is heavy I will try and lift it too
By simply asking God to help you see it through.

In hope you will face another day, when skies will glisten blue
Flowers will bloom, the birds will sing and all of this for you
Love will be around you through all of those who care –

Your family and loved ones and I will still be there
So we will face the future diminishing all fear
Trusting you to God's own care knowing He is near
Look up to the heavens
The golden sun, the singing birds
and know it's all
FOR YOU.

*Judy Thomas wrote this poem 'for a friend – a breast cancer patient –
who after treatment received another blow. Thank God she is still with
us after several years and has worked and raised money for cancer
research at Singleton.' – ed.*

Lesley Townshend-Smith
Merlyn's Story

I lay in pain on the back seat of the car and listened to the angry voices and arguments coming from the front. "It's your fault" - "You should have shut the gate"-"How much is all this going to cost?" Suddenly the car stopped and I was carried into a white room with strange smells and noises. Strong hands lifted me onto a table and a kind voice said "Let me see, what have we got here?"

The pain in my leg got worse as the lady's fingers moved it around and poked and prodded me. Then I felt a sharp stab in my neck, and the pain in my front leg began to feel better.

My name is Merlyn, and I think I'm rather handsome with my shaggy white fur and black spots. I never knew my father but my mother was a beautiful collie who helped to look after the sheep on the farm where I was born. She always said my father was the English Setter from down the valley.

I think I must have been a disappointment to her, because I didn't stay long on the farm. Before I was one I found myself in a large building with lots of other dogs-the noise and smell was unbelievable. I stayed there for a while and then went to live with my new family in town. They gave me my new name Merlyn.

That morning I had spotted my best friend the cat and ran across the road to say hello. Suddenly there was a loud hooting and squealing noise and something hit me and I flew into the air and when I opened my eyes I was lying at the side of the road in pain and unable to move.

I felt another sharp pain and gradually dozed off to sleep - I could still hear my family arguing with the nice lady. " You're joking, that's far too much, we can't afford it. Put the dog down." The voices gradually faded away and I fell asleep.

When I woke up I found my leg was trapped inside a cage and I was lying in a metal box. I felt very groggy and thirsty. I found some water and had a drink and started to look around me. I couldn't see much - just white walls. I stayed with the kind people for a very long time.

I learned to show them my poor paw and not to mind being given pills and stabbed by needles. I got used to the kind voices and all the other animals visiting. I liked that part and often tried to get into the other rooms to say hello, but I usually got found out.

My leg got better and the cage came off and I could walk again, a bit stiffly but a nice old gentleman came and took me out for walks so that I could explore the streets where I now lived.

Then one day while I was sleeping in the normal place I heard a friendly voice saying 'Hello' so I got up to see if I could get any attention. I was enjoying the pats and cuddles and half listening to the voices:

"He's gorgeous isn't he, so friendly and gentle, he can come home with me any time he likes. Really? He is looking for a home?" Ten minutes later I was in a strange car and going to a new home, just in time for Christmas.

Now I have a new family and some new friends , a little terrier called Sophie, a cat called Tubby , some chinchillas and lots of guinea pigs in my garden. I think I am a very lucky dog to have found such a good home. People here keep saying how special I am and I feel very much loved and I know that I love my new friends. I suppose that even dogs can be a blessing as well as receive them.

Biddy Wigley
The Poppy

The desert and the parched land will be glad;
the wilderness will rejoice and blossom.
Isaiah 35:1

Driving from Swansea across the Heads of the Valleys, I always
enjoy the breathtaking views. At the present time it is interesting
to see how the work, to upgrade this lovely route, is progressing.
The current phase, over the four miles between Gilwern and
Abergavenny, has involved a staggering amount of earth
movement and a lot of organisation to keep the traffic moving
reasonably freely.

I know little about road building but have observed that the
earthworks advance in phases, different strata being exposed in
turn so that all the underground work can be carried out. To
accomplish this the earth has to be moved several times
bringing landscape changes and route diversions.

Moving slowly in heavy traffic recently I studied the mounds of
sub soil and rocks along the roadside. The sub soil was grey,
arid and impoverished, the landscape having a lunar air about it.

The rocks and boulders were the remains of the old road and are, I assume, awaiting reuse as hard core for the new road. Below road level considerable work has been carried out on essential services, drainage and the foundations for bridges, in preparation for the eventual improved road – work that will be hidden once the project is complete.

In the midst of all the organised chaos of the building site, my spirits were lifted by the sight of a single red poppy perched merrily on top of a mound of stony soil. No doubt it had been disturbed several times before being left long enough to flower but what pleasure it provided in that arid landscape.

My observations made me consider the turmoil of the human condition. The 'topsoil' of our lives is often disturbed by events, and this will expose our inner condition. Once the 'tarmac' is broken up the 'rubble' of fear, worry and anxiety is exposed which can result in despair or bitterness. Rather than being overwhelmed by our circumstances we can use them and learn from them.

We can choose to let them teach us and so use the rubble in a positive way, as a foundation for developing the resilience and stamina to cope with the many strong emotions such as grief, loss, illness and disappointment which can so demoralise us.

However bleak our present seems, God has a wonderful future planned for us if we trust Him. We can develop inner peace, love and joy, the necessities of life, through fellowship with God. That poppy was a beautiful picture of the inner life of those who rest on the strength of God in the midst of the chaos of the world around, and a symbol of a future when the dry and useless will become well watered and fruitful.

When the tough times come in future I will remember that bright little poppy, encouraging the passers by from its tenuous and unenviable position. It had overcome so much yet had still persevered to become a bright yet peaceful and untroubled symbol of the serenity that is available to us.

Matthew Wright (Aged 10)
My Brother Jack
(Aged 2 and three quarters)

When my mum told me that I was going to have a baby brother I was really glad as I would have company and somebody to play with. I saw him the first time in hospital and I thought he would be really active and playing around, but he was really a bit boring! But I still loved him and when we got him home just before Christmas, all I wanted to do was to cuddle him.

I bought him a little white teddy from the shop with "You are my bestest friend" written on him because that is what I thought of him. We called him Snowy because it was two days before Christmas Day and because he was white and Jack still takes him to bed every night and we don't go away without him.

I started changing his nappies when he was a few days old, but one time, when he was about three months old, he wee'd everywhere when I went to get another nappy and I had to dive out of the way!

At six weeks' old we went to a reunion of all of mum's friends and I was jealous that he got all the attention, but I was so proud that he was my little brother. I still couldn't wait until he was older, but looking back, I wish sometimes that he was small again.

The things I like doing with Jack are playing games, jumping on each other, doing things that he likes (like opening drinks and, even better, presents!) and helping him build toys and models. I love showing him how things work and reading his favourite books to him. When we are in the garden, I love pushing him around in his car and then playing football and letting in goals, because he loves celebrating. Best of all is being a pain to mum and dad when we wind each other up!

He can be a real nuisance when he interrupts me on my Playstation and switches it off when I am in the middle of a game. Sometimes he goes into my bedroom and breaks my toys. He really is "Destructorboy". He is a pain in the back (because he jumps on my back like a horse when I watch TV).

He really likes playing in my playroom in the loft. His favourite things are the Knex roller coaster, playing games and watching Scooby Doo on TV or on the DVD in the car. He enjoys playing his guitar and singing in my shows for Mum and Dad.

I'm really looking forward to him going to my school after Christmas as I'll be able to see mum dropping him off in the yard. But it will only be for six months and then I'm going to comp.

I really love my brother, although he can be a real pain when he's tired. I love playing with him and especially I love to see him when he is asleep, 'cos he looks really cute.